The Best Day of My Life

If someone were to ask us to name the best day of our lives, most of us would cite the day we got married, the day our children were born, or some other special day we remember fondly. But how many of us would say "The best day of my life was the day I was baptized?" How many of us really think of our baptismal "birthday" as the most significant day in our lives?

Yet what could be more important than receiving the sacrament that Jesus said was necessary for our salvation? What could be more momentous than the day that we were "born again" as sons and daughters of God—the day we came to life spiritually, receiving as a gift not only the right but the ability to call the all-powerful Creator of the universe "Abba" or "Daddy?" What could be more profound than the day when the Holy Spirit came to dwell in us and we became "partakers in the divine nature?" **Yet sadly, many of us have been baptized without ever coming to understand its reality and meaning, and we, in turn, baptize our children with our eyes still veiled to the eternal significance of this sacred ritual.**

John 3:5

2 Corinthians 5:17
2 Peter 1:4

Do we understand why we need to be baptized? Do we comprehend what it "does" to us, and the eternal impact that this "bath of rebirth" has upon us? Could we explain to a curious onlooker what "happens" to us when we are baptized, and that although we look exactly the same, we are in reality dramatically different creatures after Baptism? If we are like many Catholics, we must honestly answer "no."

In *Living Water* we will:

- examine the origin, purpose, and significance of the sacrament of Baptism,

- find out how this holy sacrament was instituted by Jesus as the means through which we are incorporated into his family, the Church,

- learn about the permanent effect that Baptism has upon our souls, and how it heals us of sin and empowers us to live a Christian life,

- review the Rite of Baptism itself, and consider the deeper meaning of the words, symbols, and gestures with which we are so familiar.

Living Water will enhance your appreciation of the awesome gift God has given us in his Church, Baptism, and all the sacraments. We pray that your faith will be deepened, and that—

> [T]he eyes of your hearts [will be] enlightened, that you may know what is the hope to which he has called you . . . and what is the immeasurable greatness of his power in us who believe. **Ephesians 1:18–19**

1

The Significance of Baptism

To begin to understand the significance of Baptism, we must first recognize that Jesus felt Baptism was so important that the command to baptize others was included in the last words he said to the eleven disciples: "Go therefore and make disciples of all nations, baptizing them in the name of the Father and of the Son and of the Holy Spirit" (Matthew 28:19).

Jesus said we must be born anew.

John 3:3

CCC 1257

In his well-known conversation with the Jewish ruler Nicodemus, Jesus declared that one must be "born anew" to see the kingdom of God. Confused as to his meaning, Nicodemus questions, "How can a man be born when he is old? Can he enter a second time into his mother's womb and be born?" (John 3:4). But Jesus instructs him: "Truly, truly, I say to you, unless one is born of water and the Spirit, he cannot enter the kingdom of God" (John 3:5). The sacrament of Baptism is precisely the new birth Jesus was referring to, and Jesus' parting words affirm that Baptism is central to the mission of the apostles.

Why do we need to be born again?

CCC 386–89

This probably would have been our next question if we were conversing with Jesus. Why on earth do we *need* to be reborn if we are already alive? This question can only be answered with the help of what we call "Revelation," that is, what God has communicated to mankind over time about his plan of salvation for us.

The reality of sin

CCC 396–409

The Bible, which is God's revealed word, tells us that we are all born sinful due to the "original sin" of our first parents, Adam and Eve. St. Paul speaks of this sin when he says: "Therefore as sin came into the world through one man and death through sin, and so death spread to all men because all men sinned" (Romans 5:12).

In the beginning, man and woman were "fit" for life with God. In other words, Adam and Eve were created by God with the personal familiarity, holiness, integrity, and superabundance of grace necessary to live forever in his presence. Though God created them in a state of intimate love and friendship with him, as beloved children made in his own image and likeness, Adam and Eve freely chose to disobey their heavenly Father, committing what is known as "original sin."

Genesis 1–3

The absence of something

CCC 374–79

Original sin is not so much a thing as the absence of something. Tragically, when our first parents chose to sin against God, they lost the gift of divine nature, leaving them to live in a lesser state of existence than originally bestowed upon them by God. Their nature "fell" from a god-like state to a corrupted state, and they began to sin all the more. Worse yet, they began to experience separation from God, suffering, and physical and spiritual death, instead of the eternal life full of happiness, holiness, intimacy, and peace that God had planned for them. Sadly, they no longer interacted with God as tenderly loved children, but they began to believe that God "had it out for them," cowering in fear and shame in his presence.

Genesis 3:8–10

Our inheritance from Adam and Eve

When Adam and Eve alienated themselves from God, they infected the whole human race with sin. As a result, we are all born with the stain or birth defect of "original sin" on our souls. We come into the world separated from God and prone to do evil, instead of loving God above all else, enjoying divine friendship, and doing what is good for us and pleasing to him. St. Paul vividly describes our struggle with sin when he exclaims: "For I do not do what I want, but I do the very thing I hate. . . . Now if I do what I do not want . . . it is no longer I that do it, but sin that dwells within me" **(Romans 7:15, 17).**

Romans 7:13–20

"Where sin increased, grace abounded all the more." Romans 5:20

God in his great love and mercy did not leave us without hope. Even as the story of human sin unfolds in **Genesis 3**, God announces a Redeemer, a Savior who will come to restore man's loving relationship with his heavenly Father and enable him to overcome sin and its consequences.

Genesis 3:15–24
CCC 1008

Jesus Christ is revealed as the long-awaited Redeemer, "the new Adam," whose obedient self-offering on the Cross would reverse the disobedience of Adam and Eve, bringing the possibility of new life and a restored relationship with God to the whole human race.

Romans 5:15–19
CCC 410–12

If new life is available, how do I get it?

Though the Apostle Paul clearly teaches that Christ died to give everyone the possibility of eternal life, the question still remains: "How do I get it?" What means did God establish for us to access the victory Christ won through his death and resurrection, so that we, like Jesus, can overcome death and live eternally with God? How do we find, once again, a relationship of friendship and kinship with the Father, so we can claim the family inheritance of heaven? Let's go back to Nicodemus and his encounter with Jesus.

St. Justin Martyr, a martyr and avid defender of the apostolic faith, elaborated on the Church's understanding of Baptism in his *First Apology*, written between A.D. 148–155: **"Then they are brought by us to where there is water, and are regenerated in the same manner in which we ourselves were regenerated (reborn). For in the name of God, the Father . . . and of our Savior Jesus Christ, and of the Holy Spirit, they then receive the washing with water. For Christ said, 'Except ye be born again, ye shall not enter into the kingdom of heaven.'"**

Ephesians 2:1

Spiritual rebirth

While Nicodemus expresses confusion as to how he could be "born again," Jesus makes it clear that he is speaking of a different kind of birth, not merely earthly birth in human flesh, but supernatural rebirth, given through "water and Spirit" (John 3:6–12). Such rebirth is absolutely necessary for all people, because Revelation tells us that although we enter the world physically alive, we are spiritually "dead" due to sin. In other words, though we are alive on a natural or human level, we have ceased to possess the supernatural life within us that God intended for his children—the life that enables mere human beings to interact with their Creator as divine sons and daughters, spirit to Spirit.

CCC 1250
Ephesians 1:4

God alone can restore us to the supernatural life, and it is precisely this act of restoration that the God-man, Jesus Christ, came to accomplish for us. In short, Baptism is the only way we can become who we were intended to be before the foundation of the world.

CCC 1265, 1213

Baptism is the gateway to life.

The sacrament of Baptism was established by Christ as the means through which we are brought to life by God, wherein we become "one" with Jesus and receive the forgiveness of our sins and the gift of divine life through the Holy Spirit who comes to live within us. The Church has believed for 2,000 years that Baptism is "the gateway to life in the Spirit," and it has always understood Jesus' words to Nicodemus as a direct reference to Baptism. Just as we passed through the waters of our mother's womb to receive natural birth, so must we pass through the waters of Baptism to receive supernatural rebirth. This fundamental truth of the Christian faith is repeatedly affirmed by Jesus', as well as through the Apostles', own record of the role of Baptism in the early Church.

Bible Search

Look up specific biblical references about the importance of Baptism:

- John 3:5
- Mark 16:15–16
- Matthew 28:19–20
- Acts 2:38
- Acts 9:10–18
- Acts 16:30–33

Why did Jesus choose water?

Water symbolizes cleansing.

Jesus did not choose a meaningless symbol when instituting the sacrament of Baptism. Instead, he chose a familiar ritual that held great symbolism for his followers—the practice of washing oneself in water to signify spiritual cleansing. "Baptism," which comes from a Greek word meaning to "dip," "immerse," or "plunge," was practiced among various ancient peoples including the Jews, and always in connection with the belief that the ritual of washing oneself in water symbolized the cleansing of personal faults and spiritual impurities. Additionally, water has always been and remains a source of life and fruitfulness. Its association with the life-giving spirit of God goes back to the dawn of creation when God called forth the created realm through water and the Word.

The ordinary made extraordinary.

Through his words, and through his death and resurrection, Jesus infused a mere symbol of purification with extraordinary power, changing ordinary water to "living water" **(John 4:10)** that communicates eternal life to those washed in it. St. Paul affirms the saving power of Baptism to his disciple Titus, whom he instructs by letter: "[H]e saved us . . . by the washing of regeneration and renewal in the Holy Spirit, which he poured out upon us richly through Jesus Christ our Savior, so that we might be justified by his grace and become heirs in hope of eternal life. This saying is sure." **(Titus 3:5–8)**.

Jesus' public ministry began with Baptism.

Jesus, the sinless God-man who needed neither repentance nor forgiveness, initiated his public ministry and demonstrated the importance of Baptism by submitting himself to the Baptism of John. He did this to:

- allow himself to be numbered among sinners,
- accept and inaugurate his mission as God's suffering Servant,
- open the heavens that were once closed by Adam's sin,
- set an example of Baptism, which he would later teach as the means of being "born anew," and
- sanctify the waters to be used in the sacrament of Baptism.

Sacrament

AN OUTWARD SIGN instituted by Christ to communicate grace. In the sacraments, God makes use of his creation, taking ordinary matter and infusing it with his power, making it a conduit of grace.

CCC 1218
Genesis 1:2, 6
2 Peter 3:5–6
John 1:1–4

John 4:1–26

CCC 535

Bible Search

Scriptural references for the Baptism of Jesus.

- Matthew 3:13–17
- Mark 1:4–11
- Luke 3:15–22
- John 1:19–34

The Effects of Baptism

Mark 16:16

Baptism offers amazing grace—the forgiveness of our sins and the free and unde-served gift of eternal life won for us by Jesus Christ. Its power depends entirely on the death and resurrection of Christ, and upon his Word that faith and Baptism open the door to his heavenly kingdom.

CCC 798, 1262–67

Though the principle effects of Baptism are the forgiveness of sin (including original sin and all personal sin) and new birth in the Holy Spirit, Baptism has many radical consequences for us. Scripture reveals that when the Holy Spirit comes to dwell within us, we become members of Christ's living Body on earth[1]—completely new creatures with new natures, adopted children of God who possess new powers and new rights! Let's look at these many incredible effects.

■ Baptism restores communion with God.

Sin and death ruled over the human race until God sent his only Son to die on the Cross, taking upon himself "the sin of the world" **(John 1:29)** and overcoming death by rising from the dead. Through his death and resurrection, Jesus ushered in a new era for mankind—an era that restored us to the possibility of commun-ion with God and freedom from the dominion of death. Christ's redemptive act *repaired* the damage done by sin; opening the way for people to once again live as the Father's own sons and daughters, both now and for all eternity.

CCC 654

CCC 1010–11

We access Jesus' "repair work" through faith and Baptism, which Scripture reveals unites us to Christ's death and resurrection in so real a way that we, like our Lord, die and rise again to new life, overcoming sin and death through the victorious death and resurrection of Christ.

> "Do you not know that all of us who have been baptized into Christ Jesus were baptized into his death? We were buried therefore with him by baptism into death, so that as Christ was raised from the dead by the glory of the Father, we too might walk in newness of life." **Romans 6:3–4**
>
> "[Y]ou were buried with him in baptism, in which you were also raised with him through faith in the working of God, who raised him from the dead." **Colossians 2:12**

Now, instead of fearing death as a "curse" to be avoided at all costs, we can embrace death as a blessing—the blessed threshold through which we are called by Jesus to enter our true home, heaven.

---

[1] **1 Corinthians 12:12–13**: "For just as the body is one and has many members, and all the members of the body, though many, are one body, so it is with Christ. For by one spirit we were all baptized into one body . . . and all were made to drink of one spirit."

■ We become adopted children of God.

When we respond in faith to Jesus Christ and receive the sacrament of Baptism, not only are we unafraid of death, we are restored to the life God always desired for us, regaining the divine nature **(2 Peter 1:4)**, and the gift of sonship originally enjoyed by Adam and Eve. Regaining our status as the Father's divine children means that we are on a "first name basis" with God, and we therefore have the right to address him in the most familiar of terms as "Daddy."[2]

St. Paul tells us about this marvelous reality when he writes: "For all who are led by the Spirit of God are sons of God. For you did not receive the spirit of slavery to fall back into fear, but you received the spirit of sonship [through which] we cry *Abba,* Father!" **(Romans 8:14–15)**. As God's sons and daughters, we also begin to "bear the family resemblance," imaging God in holiness and love as we wait to claim our family inheritance, heaven.

CCC 1265

Ephesians 4:30
2 Corinthians 1:22

> **A**ROUND A.D. 189 St. Irenaeus, who was a disciple of St. Polycarp, who himself was a disciple of the beloved Apostle St. John, wrote about the gift of divine sonship in his work titled *Against Heresies*: **"For this is why the Word became man, and the Son of God became the Son of man: so that man, by entering into communion with the Word, and thus receiving divine sonship, might become a son of God"** (CCC 460).

■ It brings us into the life of the Blessed Trinity.

According to Christ's instructions, we are baptized in the name of the Father, the Son, and the Holy Spirit. Our Savior issued this command because he desires that we bear his *family name*—the name of the Holy Trinity, in whose name we become God's own people and possession.

CCC 1235, 1239

The eternal God consists of three Divine Persons—Father, Son, and Holy Spirit—and receiving the sign of these Persons (the sign of the Cross) signifies our belief in their existence and union, as well our understanding that we are birthed into their extended family by our Baptism into Christ's death and resurrection. The innermost mystery of the Divine Family is precisely *the familial love* shared among them—a love exchange between the Eternal Father and his only begotten Son that is so great that it literally overflows into a Third Person, the Holy Spirit. When we are baptized, we are granted more than a "name only" association with the Trinity; we are impregnated with the Spirit of their **love**, who comes to live within us to enable us to behave as God's family members. That means that we can now put our unwavering **faith** in God's promises, **hope** in heaven as our true home, and most importantly, love with the very love of God.

CCC 1266, 1812–29

Theological Virtues

> **G**IFTS INFUSED into the soul by God at Baptism that supernaturally empower us to behave as God's children are:
>
> - **faith**
> - **hope**
> - **love**—"the greatest of which is love" (1 Corinthians 13:13).

---

2 "Abba" is the Hebrew word for "Daddy," and it is the name we are instructed to call God in the New Covenant.

■ We become temples of the Holy Spirit.

Through Baptism, our beings are infused with God's Spirit in so profound a way that we are transformed into living "temples"—"houses of worship" whose primary purpose is to manifest God's presence, glory, and love now and for all eternity.

> "And Peter said to them, 'Repent, and be baptized every one of you in the name of Jesus Christ for the forgiveness of your sins; and you shall receive the gift of the Holy Spirit.'" **Acts 2:38**
>
> "Do you not know that your body is the temple of the Holy Spirit within you, which you have from God? You are not your own; you were bought with a price." **1 Corinthians 6:19–20**

"The Most Holy Trinity gives the baptized sanctifying grace, the grace of *justification*:

- enabling them to believe in God, to hope in him, and to love him through the theological virtues;

- giving them the power to live and act under the prompting of the Holy Spirit through the gifts of the Holy Spirit; and

CCC 1266

- allowing them to grow in goodness through the moral virtues."

■ We become a new creation.

Once we receive God's name and God's Spirit, we no longer belong to ourselves, but we become the sacred property of the One who has taken up residence within us. Because we are God's possession, he makes his mark on us, sealing us with an indelible imprint of the Holy Spirit that remains with us eternally and identifies us as one who belongs to God. The "seal of the Spirit" can never be lost, and because it is permanent, can never be given again. We become a "partaker in the divine nature,"[3] a member of Christ and co-heir with him. We change not only in "status," we change in our very nature becoming new creatures in Christ. Baptism gives us the very character of Christ, empowering us to live as his Body on earth, sharing God's love and the good news of faith in Jesus Christ to all we meet.

---

[3] **2 Peter 1:4**.

■ We become living members of the Body of Christ his Church.

Baptism incorporates us into Christ's Body, the Church, which is the "living" extension of his resurrected and glorified Body now in heaven.

2 Corinthians 5:17

> "[A]nd he has put all things under his feet and has made him the head over all things for the church, which is his body, the fulness of him who fills all in all." **Ephesians 1:22–23**

Although Jesus' physical presence was taken from his disciples at the Ascension, he promised to send the Holy Spirit, who would form them into one Body on earth—a Body through which Jesus could continue to live and act in the world to call all people to receive divine sonship and eternal life through faith and Baptism.

"Now you are the body of Christ and individually parts of it." 1 Corinthians 12:27

Belonging to the Body of Christ means that we are intimately connected with the Body's Head, Jesus Christ, and with all who have made up its members since the inception of the Church. As such, we receive the prerogative of calling upon the whole Body to help us.

ALL PEOPLE WHO BELIEVE in Christ and have been properly baptized belong to Christ's Body, the Church. This includes those who belong to Christian denominations that exist outside of the Catholic faith. The Catholic Church recognizes as valid all baptisms that are performed in faith using a Trinitarian formula and either sprinkling, pouring or immersion in water. **CCC 818, 1271**

The Rights and Duties of the Baptized

CCC 818, 1271

The Church teaches that, by virtue of our Baptism, laypeople are made participants in Christ's offices of priest, prophet, and king. How each baptized person will live out these offices depends on their particular mission and call. But *whether* each baptized person is called to do so is not a question. These offices are common to every baptized person—even to baptized non-Catholics—for it is inherent in the nature of Christian Baptism.

"Go, and do not sin again." John 8:11

CCC 1264, 1426

Though we receive superabundant graces and blessings when we are "born anew," there are "temporal" or temporary consequences of sin that remain with us throughout our time on earth. These consequences include the frailty of our human nature, suffering, physical death, and the tendency to sin.

Although faith and Baptism restore us to the divine life and the grace of sonship, it is a reality that we continue to live in a fallen world, and will do so until God calls us home in death or Christ returns in glory. Due to this fact, our journey through this life involves an ongoing struggle with sin, and the realization that it can reoccur in our lives. The good news is that our merciful Father is always ready to forgive us, and he has provided for our lapses into sin through the sacrament of Reconciliation.[4] As the Apostle John explains it, "If we say we have no sin, we deceive ourselves and the truth is not in us. If we confess our sins, he is faithful and just, and will forgive our sins and cleanse us from all unrighteousness" (1 John 1:8–9).

"Be holy because I [am] holy." 1 Peter 1:16

Something holy is that which is set apart for God and united to God. Our personal holiness is both a *gift* and a *calling*. We are made holy through our Baptism and we are also called to live as holy people according to the teachings of Christ.

Ephesians 4:22–24

We are called and empowered by God to "be holy yourselves in all your conduct" (1 Peter 1:15) and to "grow in the grace and knowledge of our Lord and Savior Jesus Christ" (2 Peter 3:18). Throughout our new life, we are called to put off our sinful ways and to put on the Lord Jesus Christ.

How do we do this?

- Through obedience to the Word of God and his Church
- By faithful reception of the sacraments
- By yielding our lives to the transforming work of the Holy Spirit within us

---

4 The Apostles were given explicit authority by Christ to forgive sins. **John 20:22–23**: "[H]e breathed on them and said to them, 'Receive the Holy Spirit. If you forgive the sins of any, they are forgiven; if you retain the sins of any, they are retained.'"

The Baptismal Rite

Now that we have learned what Baptism is and what it does to us, we can take a look at the key components of the baptismal "rite" or ceremony itself, investigating the deeper meaning of the various elements that are part of this sacred ritual. The signs and gestures of the baptismal rite make the meaning of the sacrament and the graces it communicates evident to us, as each and every word and sign that is employed in Baptism carries its own significance and points us to the Pascal Mystery.

We will follow the movements for the rite of Baptism for children, because the majority of baptisms that take place within the Catholic Church involve infants and young children. Adults and children over the age of seven are usually received into the Church at the Easter Vigil, where they receive all three sacraments of Initiation at once (Baptism, Confirmation, and Eucharist). The Baptism of younger children occurs throughout the year, either within the celebration of the Sunday Liturgy or privately.

The Power of the Sacraments

JESUS ESTABLISHED the sacraments as the tangible means on earth through which we receive God's grace. The sacraments are much more than mere symbols—they are "graced encounters" with God that empower us to grow in Christian maturity.

In other words, God acts in and through the sacraments to bring about our continued transformation. Our job is simply to receive the gifts and graces he freely gives, coming with willing hearts and open hands to allow God to continue to heal us and transform us into his image.

The Reception of the Child by the Church

The celebration of Baptism begins as the father and mother, accompanied by the godparents, present the child to the Church. The celebrating priest or deacon addresses the parents and godparents about their intentions concerning the child's faith, as it is their cooperative responsibility to transmit the Catholic faith to the child.

The celebrant first asks the parents if it is their intention to accept the responsibility of raising the child to practice the Catholic faith, reminding them that it is their duty to train the child to obey all that Christ teaches through his Church. Parents must affirm their clear understanding of the responsibility they are undertaking at Baptism, as this "sacrament of faith" implants within a child the gift of faith that must be nurtured and developed over time through active participation in the life of the Church. The celebrant then addresses the godparents, asking if they will readily assist the parents as they fulfill their duty in raising the child in the Catholic faith. Once the parents and godparents answer affirmatively, the priest or deacon claims the child for Christ through the Sign of the Cross.

Godparents

MATURE CHRISTIAN adults who publicly commit to assist the newly baptized to continue to grow in the Catholic faith throughout their lives. Though parents bear the primary responsibility as educators and models of the faith, godparents are also called to play an active role in ongoing Christian formation, as they cooperate with parents in encouraging and "growing up" the faith of young believers.

■ The Sign of the Cross (CCC 1235)

The celebrant and the parents now trace the Sign of the Cross onto the forehead of the baptismal candidate, placing the imprint of the source of salvation—the Cross of Christ—onto the one who will be received into his Body. Marking a baptismal candidate with the Sign of the Cross identifies him as one who will soon belong to God, enabling him to say with St. Paul:

> "I bear on my body the marks of Jesus." **Galatians 6:17**

Revelation 7:3

From the earliest days of the Church, the ceremonies used to initiate Christians into the Body of Christ included tracing the Cross onto the forehead of "catechumens," or those receiving instruction in the faith in preparation for their formal entrance into the Church through the sacraments of Initiation. Even the book of Revelation, written before A.D. 90, makes reference to the servants of God who have had God's seal put on their foreheads, demonstrating the familiarity of the apostolic Church with this practice. The Sign of the Cross expresses our faith in the potency of Christ's Cross. It also provides ongoing protection against temptation, as we make the Sign of the Cross throughout our lives to renew our commitment to our Savior.

Liturgy of the Word

◼ The Proclamation of God's Word

CCC 1236, 1253

Next, we arrive at the "Liturgy of the Word, a segment of the baptismal rite where God's Word is proclaimed to those assembled through various Scripture readings. Hearing the truths of salvation declared aloud through the Word of God elicits in all gathered the response of active faith—faith that is absolutely necessary for salvation, as made clear by the Council of Trent, which stated: "Besides a wish to be baptized, in order to obtain the grace of the sacrament, faith is also necessary."[5]

In the case of infant Baptism, the faith of the parents and the whole Church "stands in proxy" for the faith of the infant, as the Church asks God to implant the gift of faith in the child. The faith that the child receives is thus a "seed" of faith; faith that is called to grow and develop to perfect and mature faith over time. The entire Church must therefore support, safeguard, and fertilize such beginning faith until it reaches full maturity.

◼ The Intercessions and The Litany of the Saints

"Holy Mary, Mother of God . . . pray for us"

The Church now prays for the needs of the child and his family, asking God to continue to bless them and keep them faithful to the Gospel. The Church especially asks for the intercession of the saints, calling upon the help of those who have gone before us to heaven to request their prayers and assistance. This is known as "the Litany of the Saints," and it usually includes the names of patron saints of those being baptized, along with other great heroes of the Catholic faith.

The Church has long understood the power of intercessory prayer,[6] and the practice of invoking the help of the saints in prayer goes back to the earliest days of the Church. It expresses our belief in the "Communion of Saints," which is the real spiritual union that is shared by all of the members of the Body of Christ, including those who have preceded us in death who are now perfectly united to Christ in heaven. Requesting the help of the whole Body of Christ draws us closer to Christ, who is the Head of the Body and the source of all of its power.

CCC 956–57

---

[5] *The Catechism of the Council of Trent* (Rockford, Ill: Tan Books, 1982), p. 181.

[6] **James 5:16**: "The prayer of a righteous man has great power in its effects." Who is more righteous than those perfectly united to Christ in heaven?

■ Prayer of Exorcism

> "Almighty and ever-living God, you sent your only Son into the world to cast out the power of Satan, spirit of evil, to rescue man from the kingdom of darkness . . . we pray for this child: set him free from original sin, make him a temple of your glory. . . ."

Following the intercessions, the celebrant may speak "exorcisms" over the child, using words similar to the above. These are "prayers through which the Church asks publicly and authoritatively in the name of Jesus Christ that a person or object be protected against the power of the Evil One and withdrawn from his dominion."

Jesus performed exorcisms on many people, and he gave his apostles the authority to do likewise: "He appointed twelve to be with him and to be sent to preach and have authority to cast out demons" **(Mark 3:14)**. Exorcism is an exercise of the spiritual authority entrusted to the Church by Jesus, which frees a person so they may fully serve Christ.

■ Anointing before Baptism

Once the prayer of exorcism is concluded, a pre-baptismal anointing with the "oil of catechumens" is administered to the child. Anointing a person with oil, in biblical symbolism, is a sign of abundance and joy, as well as a symbol of healing and strengthening. The practice of anointing was used in the Old Testament to "set apart" or "make sacred" a person or thing for God. It was administered to people, places, and things, including God's priests, the Ark of the Covenant, and the tent of meeting and its furniture. Oil was also used to anoint the great kings of Israel, including Saul, David, and Solomon, marking them for God's service.

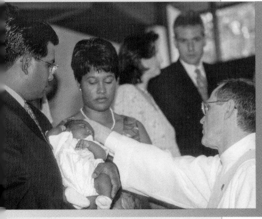

2 Corinthians 1:21–22

Anointing the child with oil blessed by the bishop, who is a direct successor of the Apostles, is a sign of the "anointing in the Holy Spirit"—an anointing that marks them as God's "sacred" possessions, and sets them apart for his purposes and his glory. The anointing received at Baptism is a permanent one that not only identifies the baptized as God's own people through the "seal" of his Spirit, it provides healing from sin, an abundance of God's holy presence, and continual strengthening in the life of faith so those baptized into Christ may "remain in Him" **(1 John 2:24–27)**. The celebrant thus prays over the child:

> "We anoint you with the oil of salvation in the name of Christ our Savior; may he strengthen you with his power, who lives and reigns for ever and ever. Amen."

Bible Search

Look up specific Old Testament references about the practice of anointing:

- **Exodus 30:25** *ff.*
- **1 Samuel 10:1**
- **1 Samuel 16:13**
- **1 Kings 1:39**

Celebration of the Sacrament

CCC 1238

■ The Blessing of the Baptismal Waters

The minister now blesses the waters to be used in the Baptism, touching the water with his right hand to call down God's life-giving power upon it. The minister prays the following (or similar) words, acknowledging the active presence of the Three Persons of the Trinity in the sacrament of Baptism.

> "We ask you, Father, with your Son to send the Holy Spirit upon the waters of this font. May all who are buried with Christ in the death of baptism rise with him to the newness of life."

Water has always been a sign of natural and spiritual life, and its immediate association with the Spirit of God goes back to the beginning of creation. In Baptism, the Church asks the Father, through his eternal Son, to send the Holy Spirit upon water so that those washed in it may be "born of water and the Spirit." According to Jesus' own words, without this rebirth, we "cannot enter the kingdom of God" **(John 3:5)**. Such rebirth, which is found in the sacrament of Baptism, is "prefigured" in the Old Testament through the great events of salvation history, especially those events that use water to display God's life-giving power.

CCC 1237

■ The Renunciation of Sin

After the water is blessed, the parents and godparents are asked to explicitly renounce sin and Satan on the child's behalf, formally disassociating the child from "the father of lies" **(John 8:44)** and aligning him with Jesus, "the source of eternal salvation" **(Hebrews 5:9)**. Parents and godparents also renew their own baptismal promises at this time by answering "I do" to the following (or similar) questions, indicating their desire and intent to remain free of the poison of sin:

- "Do you reject sin so as to live in the freedom of God's children?
- Do you reject the glamour of evil, and refuse to be mastered by sin?
- Do you reject Satan, father of sin and prince of darkness?"

Bible Search

Prefigurements of Baptism in the Old Covenant

Look up the following scriptural references to learn about the many events in the history of salvation that "foreshadow" Baptism. (CCC 1217–1222)

- Creation **(Genesis 1:2)**
- Noah's Ark **(1 Peter 3:20–21)**
- Crossing the Red Sea **(Exodus 14:13-31)**
- Crossing of the River Jordan **(Joshua 3:5-4:7)**

Though Baptism heals us of original sin and all actual sin,[7] the baptized are called to continually strive to overcome sin through ongoing conversion to Christ. A key to such conversion lies in the sacramental life of the Church, particularly in the sacrament of the Eucharist, which heals us of venial sin, and the sacrament of Reconciliation, which heals us of mortal sin and restores us to the life of grace.[8]

---

[7] Because children under the age of reason do not commit actual sin, Baptism heals them of original sin only. In the case of adults and children over the age of reason, Baptism heals original sin and all actual sin up to the moment of Baptism.

[8] Though all sin offends God and hurts us, Scripture differentiates between mortal sin, which destroys the life of grace in the soul, and venial sin, which wounds our relationship with God without destroying it. See **1 John 5:16–17**.

■ The Profession of Faith

CCC 1237, 185, 197

Having renounced sin, the parents and godparents are now asked to confess the "faith of the Church," which is expressed in an ancient baptismal formula known as the Creed. The word "Creed," which comes from a Latin word meaning "I believe," grew out of the Trinitarian formula that was used in the earliest days of the Church to prepare catechumens for Baptism. It summarized the most important truths of the faith that were handed down by the Apostles, affirming the belief in the three Divine Persons of the Trinity and their particular actions in the history of creation and redemption. The Creeds that the Catholic Church confesses are the Apostles' Creed, which has its origin in the Apostles themselves, and the Nicene Creed, which expands on the Apostles' Creed and was approved by the Council of Nicea in A.D. 325.

The parents and godparents affirm their belief in the various parts of the Creed by answering "I do" to the following (or similar) questions:

- Do you believe in God, the Father almighty, creator of heaven and earth?

- Do you believe in Jesus Christ, his only Son, our Lord, who was born of the Virgin Mary, was crucified, died, and was buried, rose from the dead, and is now seated at the right hand of the Father?

- Do you believe in the Holy Spirit, the holy catholic Church, the communion of saints, the forgiveness of sins, the resurrection of the body, and life everlasting?

Affirming one's belief in the Church's Creed consists of more than a mere recital of words. It involves an *act* of faith, which is the total surrender of oneself and one's life to the person of Jesus Christ and to the truth he came to reveal. A person's confession of faith thus means that they assent with the entirety of their beings to the truth God has made known to us; the truth transmitted from generation to generation in all of its fullness through the Church—which Scripture calls **"the pillar and foundation of truth" (1 Timothy 3:15)**.

■ The Baptism in Water

The child is now ready for the essential part of the baptismal rite: the plunging in water for the "washing of regeneration and renewal by the Holy Spirit." Water is the primary symbol used in Baptism, as it makes readily apparent to us the effects of the sacrament, namely interior cleansing and new birth in the Holy Spirit.

The baptismal candidate's immersion in water signifies first and foremost his immersion into the death and resurrection of Christ, which obliterates his sin and allows him to share in the life-giving love of the Trinity. The waters of Baptism also symbolize the interior change that takes place within his or her soul—the transformation promised by God through the prophet Ezekiel, who said:

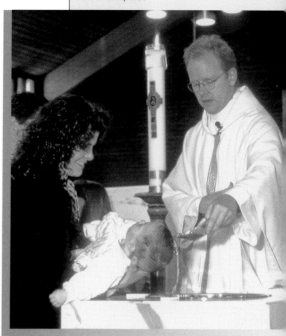

> "Thus says the Lord God. . . . I will sprinkle clean water upon you, and you shall be clean from all your uncleannesses . . . A new heart I will give you, and a new spirit I will put within you. . . . I will put my spirit within you, and cause you to walk in my statutes and be careful to observe my ordinances." **Ezekiel 36:22–27**

We find this "clean water" in the sacrament of Baptism, which transforms us from the inside out—as God's grace descends upon us and "causes" us to obey him through the indwelling presence of his Spirit. The Holy Spirit comes as a baptismal candidate is "bathed" in water three times as the minister invokes the Trinity, saying:

- **"I baptize you in the name of the Father"** (the minister immerses the child or pours water upon him),

- **"and of the Son"** (the minister immerses or pours water on the child a second time),

- **"and of the Holy Spirit"** (he immerses or pours water on the child a third time).

Baptism can take place through partial immersion, which is administered by pouring or sprinkling water on the head only, or full immersion, which is administered by plunging the entire body into water.

CCC 1215, 1239

■ The Invocation of the Holy Trinity

Alongside pouring or immersion in water, Baptism includes invoking or "calling down" the Trinity through the names of the Father, the Son, and the Holy Spirit, conferring upon the child God's own family name.

Exodus 3:13–14
Exodus 33:11 *ff.*

In the Old Testament, God's name was considered to be so holy that it couldn't even be spoken aloud, and the disclosure of God's name to his people meant that he intended to engage them in a personal, intimate relationship with him. "Yahweh" first revealed his name to Moses, a chosen leader who enjoyed such familiarity with God that he was called God's "intimate friend." God spoke to Moses "face to face" and manifested the divine presence to him in so profound a way that Moses had to veil his face to hide God's glory when he returned from his personal encounters with Yahweh.

Moses' relationship with God offers a glimpse of what God does for us in Baptism, where we not only learn God's name—*we receive it*—becoming children of the Father, brothers and sisters of Jesus Christ, and dwelling places of the Holy Spirit. We, like Moses, become bearers of God's glory, but it does not reside only on our faces. Instead God's presence fills our entire beings, making us "children of light" capable of "all that is good and right and true" **(Ephesians 5:8–9)**. As such, we are instructed *not* to veil our faces, but are told by Jesus to let our "light so shine before men, that they may see your good works and give glory to your Father who is in heaven" **(Matthew 5:16)**.

Explanatory Rites

CCC 1241, 1293, 783–86

■ The Anointing with Oil

Following Baptism, a second anointing with "sacred chrism" invests the child into the threefold offices of Jesus Christ—**priest, prophet, and king**. The minister prays the following (or similar) words as he anoints the newly baptized child:

> "God the Father of our Lord Jesus Christ has freed you from sin, given you a new birth by water and the Holy Spirit, and welcomed you into his holy people. He now anoints you with the chrism of salvation. As Christ was anointed Priest, Prophet, and King, so may you live always as a member of his body, sharing everlasting life."

All of the baptized participate in the priestly, prophetic, and kingly offices of Christ. Because of this, we are all called by Christ to:

Romans 12:1

- share in his High Priesthood, offering ourselves and our lives to the eternal Father as "living sacrifice(s), holy and pleasing to God;"

- take part in his prophetic ministry as we proclaim the Gospel, announcing to all "the wonderful deeds of him who called you out of darkness into his marvelous light;"

1 Peter 2:9

- share in the Royal Office of Jesus, serving Christ the King in all we do as we prepare to reign with him for all eternity in heaven.

■ The Baptismal Garment

CCC 1243

Having become a member of God's "royal priesthood," the baptized child is now clothed in a white garment, indicating that he has "put on Christ" **(Galatians 3:27)**. Baptismal garments were once worn by the newly baptized for the entire Easter season, demonstrating the belief that they had been "washed clean" by the Blood of Christ **(Revelation 7:9–14)**. During the baptismal rite, the garment is placed upon them by their parents and godparents, as the minister prays the words:

> "You have become a new creation and have clothed yourselves in Christ. See in this white garment the outward sign of your Christian dignity. With your family and friends to help you by word and example, bring that dignity unstained into the everlasting life of heaven. Amen."

The baptismal garment also represents the wedding gown of the Bride of Christ, the Church, as she makes herself ready for her marriage to the Heavenly Bridegroom at the end of time. At that time, all who belong to Christ will participate in an eternal "wedding feast" in heaven **(Revelation 19:7–8)**—a feast that begins now on earth as we are incorporated into the Church, and as we are given the privilege of consuming the sublime food of the wedding banquet—the Body and Blood of Christ.

■ The Lighting of the Baptismal Candle

The baptismal rite concludes with the lighting of a candle, given to the newly baptized by their parents and godparents as the minister says:

> "Parents and godparents, this light is entrusted to you to be kept burning brightly. This child of yours has been enlightened by Christ. He is to walk always as a child of the light. May he keep the flame of faith alive in his heart. When the Lord comes, may he go out to meet him with all the saints in the heavenly kingdom."

> ST. JUSTIN MARTYR wrote about the connection of Baptism and the Eucharist in his *First Apology*, written around A.D. 148–155: **"And this food is called Eucharist, of which no one is allowed to partake but the man who believes the things which we teach are true, and has been washed in the washing (bath) that is for the remission of sins, and unto regeneration, and who is living as Christ has enjoined."**

The lit candle indicates that the baptized child has been enlightened in his understanding of the truth and is now fully equipped to share the light of Christ with others. Baptism, also called "enlightenment," transfers the child from darkness into the kingdom of light, wherein he is made fit "to share in the inheritance of the saints in light" **(Colossians 1:12–13)**. This inheritance, the "birthright" of the children of God, is heaven, which the baptized begin to experience here on earth as we allow God to transform us ever more into his image and likeness—the original image of holiness, sonship, and divinity lost in Adam and restored to us through the "new Adam," Christ Jesus. The birthright of God's children also includes calling upon the eternal Creator as "Father," and it is thus that the baptismal ceremony concludes with the prayer that Christ taught us to pray: "Our Father, who art in heaven, hallowed be thy name. . . ."

Infant Baptism

"Let the children come to me." Mark 10:14

Now that we have journeyed through the baptismal rite and learned of its rich and varied symbolism, we will examine why the Church baptizes infants—a practice that has been part of Catholic tradition since the founding of the Church almost 2,000 years ago. Though infant Baptism seems natural and fitting to Catholics, many Protestant denominations have rejected the practice, claiming that a person must be able to make an adult profession of faith in order to receive Baptism.

CCC 1243, 1216

The Gospel of Mark gives us a view into our Savior's heart concerning children:

> "And they were bringing children to him that he might touch them, and the disciples rebuked them. But when Jesus saw it he was indignant and said to them, 'Let the children come to me, do not hinder them; for to such belongs the kingdom of God.'"
> **Mark 10:13–14**

This account of Jesus and the children sums up the Catholic Church's view on infant Baptism, as the Church has always hastened to baptize young children that they may be "brought into the realm of the freedom of the children of God, to which all men are called."

CCC 1250

Infant Baptism in the Early Church

The validity of infant Baptism is affirmed not only by the words of Jesus, but also by the scriptural record of the earliest days of the Church, which repeatedly indicates that whole "households" were baptized—households that must have included children, as many of ours do. In addition to that, St. Paul teaches that Baptism replaces circumcision, which was administered to infants eight days of age to incorporate them into the Old Covenant. Would a New Covenant—a new and better Covenant—suddenly exclude children, who had previously been included in the Old Covenant? The obvious answer is that children are welcomed by God in both Covenants, hence we find infant circumcision and infant Baptism as the ordinary practice of God's people.

Acts 16:15, 33, 18:8
1 Corinthians 1:16
Colossians 2:11–12

AROUND A.D. 230, the renowned biblical scholar and theologian Origen wrote: **"The Church received from the Apostles the tradition of giving Baptism even to infants. For the Apostles, to whom were committed the secrets of divine mysteries, knew that there is in everyone the innate stains of sin, which must be washed away through water and Spirit."**

God's Free Gift

The Baptism of infants also unequivocally demonstrates that it is God's grace—and not our works—that brings us to salvation in the first place. Salvation is a free and undeserved gift from God; a gift that we "receive" by putting our faith in God's Word and in his promises: "Repent and be baptized, every one of you . . . and you shall receive the gift of the Holy Spirit. For the promise is to you and to your children and to all that are far off, everyone whom the Lord our God calls to him" **(Acts 2:38–39)**. The Lord has called, and we have responded. May we continue to answer his call by growing in love and holiness throughout our lives, and may we always stand in grateful amazement at the wonderful gift our merciful Father has given us in the sacrament of Baptism.

Baptism is God's most beautiful and magnificent gift. . . .

We call it gift, grace, anointing, enlightenment,

garment of immortality, bath of rebirth,

seal, and most precious gift.

It is called **gift** because it is conferred on those

who bring nothing of their own;

grace because it is even given to the guilty;

Baptism because sin is buried in the water;

anointing for it is priestly and royal

as are those who are anointed;

enlightenment because it radiates light;

clothing since it veils our shame;

bath because it washes;

and **seal** as it is our guard and

the sign of God's Lordship.

St. Gregory of Nazianzus
Doctor of the Church
A.D. *January 6, 381*
CCC 1216

Now that I know this, what can I do?

The goal of this presentation is to unveil your eyes to the great gifts we have received in Baptism, and encourage you to see with "the eyes of faith" all that transpires when you witness the celebration of Baptism. The following discussion questions are designed to enhance your awareness of the material presented. Also included are suggestions for how you can apply this teaching to your own life, whether you are considering Baptism, are already baptized, preparing to baptize your children, or preparing to be a godparent.

Discussion Questions

1. How has this presentation on Baptism deepened your understanding of how we are fundamentally changed through this sacrament? What aspects of Baptism are most significant to you?

_____

_____

_____

_____

_____

_____

2. Why do we need to be born again through Baptism?

_____

_____

_____

_____

_____

3. What are the consequences of original sin that all people face?

_____

_____

_____

_____

4. What are the effects of Baptism?

_____

_____

_____

_____

_____